G000230429

The
King's
Breakfast

The King's Breakfast

A selection of verse from
'When We Were Very Young'

A. A. Milne

Illustrations by E. H. Shepard

METHUEN CHILDREN'S BOOKS
LONDON

First published in Great Britain in 1984 by
Methuen Children's Books Ltd,
11 New Fetter Lane, London EC4P 4EE.
This selection from WHEN WE WERE VERY YOUNG
copyright © 1984 by Michael John Brown, Peter
Janson-Smith, Roger Hugh Vaughan Charles Morgan,
and Timothy Robinson, the Trustees of
the Pooh Properties. Text by A.A. Milne, and
line illustrations by E.H. Shepard copyright
under the Berne Convention. Colouring in
by Zena Flax copyright © 1984 by Methuen
Children's Books Ltd.

Design and colouring in of illustrations by
Zena Flax Associates.

ISBN 0 416 50590 2

Printed in Great Britain by
Hazell Watson & Viney Ltd
Member of the BPCC Group
Aylesbury, Bucks

Contents

Jonathan Jo   7

Nursery Chairs   10

The Four Friends   14

The King's Breakfast   17

At the Zoo   23

Bad Sir Brian Botany   25

Puppy and I   29

Missing   32

Disobedience   35

The Three Foxes   38

Market Square   41

The Dormouse and the Doctor   45

Jonathan Jo

Jonathan Jo
Has a mouth like an "O"
And a wheelbarrow full of surprises;
If you ask for a bat,
Or for something like that,
He has got it, whatever the size is.

If you're wanting a ball,
It's no trouble at all;
Why, the more that you ask for, the merrier –
Like a hoop, and a top,
And a watch that won't stop,
And some sweets, and an Aberdeen terrier.

Jonathan Jo
Has a mouth like an "O,"
But this is what makes him so funny.
If you give him a smile,
Only once in a while,
Then he never expects any money!

Nursery Chairs

One of the chairs is South America,
  One of the chairs is a ship at sea,
One is a cage for a great big lion,
  And one is a chair for Me.

The First Chair

When I go up the Amazon,
I stop at night and fire a gun
  To call my faithful band.
And Indians in twos and threes,
Come silently between the trees,
  And wait for me to land.
And if I do not want to play
With any Indians to-day,
  I simply wave my hand.
And then they turn and go away –
  They always understand.

The Second Chair

I'm a great big lion in my cage,
   And I often frighten Nanny with a roar.
      Then I hold her very tight, and
      Tell her not to be so frightened –
   And she doesn't be so frightened
          any more.

The Third Chair

When I am in my ship, I see
   The other ships go sailing by.
A sailor leans and calls to me
   As his ship goes sailing by.
Across the sea he leans to me,
   Above the wind I hear him cry:
"Is this the way to Round-the-World?"
   He calls as he goes by.

The Fourth Chair

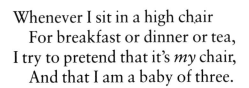

Whenever I sit in a high chair
   For breakfast or dinner or tea,
I try to pretend that it's *my* chair,
   And that I am a baby of three.

Shall I go off to South America?
   Shall I put out in my ship to sea?
Or get in my cage and be lions and tigers?
Or — shall I be only Me?

The Four Friends

Ernest was an elephant, a great big fellow,
  Leonard was a lion with a six-foot tail,
George was a goat, and his beard was yellow,
    And James was a very small snail.

Leonard had a stall, and a great big strong one,
  Ernest had a manger, and its walls were thick,
George found a pen, but I think it was the wrong one,
    And James sat down on a brick.

Ernest started trumpeting, and cracked his manger,
Leonard started roaring, and shivered his stall,
James gave the huffle of a snail in danger
        And nobody heard him at all.

Ernest started trumpeting and raised such a rumpus,
Leonard started roaring and trying to kick,
James went a journey with the goat's new compass
        And he reached the end of his brick.

Ernest was an elephant and very well-intentioned,
Leonard was a lion with a brave new tail,
George was a goat, as I think I have mentioned,
But James was only a snail.

The King's Breakfast

The King asked
The Queen, and
The Queen asked
The Dairymaid:
"Could we have some butter for
The Royal slice of bread?"

The Queen asked
The Dairymaid,
The Dairymaid
Said, "Certainly,
I'll go and tell
The cow
Now
Before she goes to bed."

The Dairymaid
She curtsied,

And went and told
The Alderney:
"Don't forget the butter for
The Royal slice of bread."

The Alderney
Said sleepily:
"You'd better tell
His Majesty
That many people nowadays
Like marmalade
Instead."

The Dairymaid
Said, "Fancy!"
And went to
Her Majesty.
She curtsied to the Queen, and
She turned a little red:

"Excuse me,
Your Majesty,
For taking of
The liberty,
But marmalade is tasty, if
It's very
Thickly
Spread."

The Queen said
"Oh!"
And went to
His Majesty:
"Talking of the butter for
The royal slice of bread,
Many people
Think that
Marmalade
Is nicer.
Would you like to try a little
Marmalade
Instead?"

The King said,
"Bother!"
And then he said,
"Oh, deary me!"
The King sobbed, "Oh, deary me!"
And went back to bed.
"Nobody,"
He whimpered,
"Could call me
A fussy man;
I *only* want
A little bit
Of butter for
My bread!"

The Queen said,
"There, there!"
And went to
The Dairymaid.
The Dairymaid
Said, "There, there!"
And went to the shed.
The cow said,
"There, there!
I didn't really
Mean it;
Here's milk for his porringer
And butter for his bread."

The Queen took
The butter
And brought it to
His Majesty;
The King said,
"Butter, eh?"
And bounced out of bed.

"Nobody," he said,
As he kissed her
Tenderly,
"Nobody," he said,
As he slid down
The banisters,
"Nobody,
My darling,
Could call me
A fussy man –
BUT
I do like a little bit of butter to my bread!"

At the Zoo

There are lions and roaring tigers, and enormous
    camels and things,
There are biffalo-buffalo-bisons, and a great big bear
    with wings,
There's a sort of tiny potamus, and a tiny
    nosserus too -
But *I* gave buns to the elephant when *I*
    went down to the Zoo!

There are badgers and bidgers and bodgers, and a
    Super-in-tendent's House,
There are masses of goats, and a Polar, and different kinds
    of mouse,
And I think there's a sort of a something which is called a wallaboo –
But *I* gave buns to the elephant when *I* went down to the Zoo!

If you try to talk to the bison, he never quite understands;
You can't shake hands with a mingo – he doesn't like
    shaking hands.
And lions and roaring tigers *hate* saying, "How do you do?" –
But *I* give buns to the elephant when *I* go down to the Zoo!

Bad
Sir Brian
Botany

Sir Brian had a battleaxe with great big knobs on;
  He went among the villagers and blipped them on the head.
On Wednesday and on Saturday, but mostly on the latter day,
  He called at all the cottages, and this is what he said:

> "I am Sir Brian!" (*ting-ling*)
> "I am Sir Brian!" (*rat-tat*)
> "I am Sir Brian, as bold as a lion —
>   Take *that!* — and *that!* — and *that!*"

Sir Brian had a pair of boots with great big spurs on,
　A fighting pair of which he was particularly fond.
On Tuesday and on Friday, just to make the street look tidy,
　He'd collect the passing villagers and kick them in the pond.

　　"I am Sir Brian!" (*sper-lash!*)
　　　"I am Sir Brian!" (*sper-losh!*)
　　"I am Sir Brian, as bold as a lion —
　　　Is anyone else for a wash?"

　　Sir Brian woke one morning, and he couldn't find his battleaxe;
　　　He walked into the village in his second pair of boots.
　　He had gone a hundred paces, when the street was full of faces,
　　　And villagers were round him with ironical salutes.

　　　　"You are Sir Brian? Indeed!
　　　　　You are Sir Brian? Dear, dear!
　　　　You are Sir Brian, as bold as a lion?
　　　　　Delighted to meet you here!"

Sir Brian went a journey, and found a lot of duck-weed:

They pulled him out and dried him, and they blipped
                                    him on the head.
They took him by the breeches, and they hurled him
                                    into ditches,
And they pushed him under waterfalls, and this is
                                    what they said:

"You are Sir Brian – don't laugh,
    You are Sir Brian – don't cry;
You are Sir Brian, as bold as a lion –
    Sir Brian, the lion, good-bye!"

Sir Brian struggled home again, and chopped up his battleaxe,
    Sir Brian took his fighting boots, and threw them in the fire.
He is quite a different person now he hasn't got his spurs on,
    And he goes about the village as B. Botany, Esquire.

"I am Sir Brian? Oh, *no!*
    I am Sir Brian? Who's he?
I haven't got any title, I'm Botany –
    Plain Mr Botany (B)."

Puppy and I

I met a Man as I went walking;
We got talking,
Man and I.
"Where are you going to, Man?" I said
   (I said to the Man as he went by).
"Down to the village, to get some bread.
   Will you come with me?"
                  "No, not I."

I met a Horse as I went walking;
We got talking,
Horse and I.
"Where are you going to, Horse, to-day?"
   (I said to the Horse as he went by).
"Down to the village to get some hay.
   Will you come with me?"
          "No, not I."

I met a Woman as I went walking;
We got talking,
Woman and I.
"Where are you going to, Woman,
    so early?"
  (I said to the Woman as she went by).
"Down to the village to get some barley.
  Will you come with me?" "No, not I."

I met some Rabbits as I went walking;
We got talking,
Rabbits and I.
"Where are you going in your brown fur coats?"
  (I said to the Rabbits as they went by).
"Down to the village to get some oats.
  Will you come with us?" "No, not I."

I met a Puppy as I went walking;
We got talking,
Puppy and I.
"Where are you going this nice fine day?"
  (I said to the Puppy as he went by).
"Up in the hills to roll and play."
   "*I'll* come with you, Puppy," said I.

Missing

Has anybody seen my mouse?

I opened his box for half a minute,
Just to make sure he was really in it,
And while I was looking, he jumped outside!
I tried to catch him, I tried, I tried . . .
I think he's somewhere about the house.
Has *anyone* seen my mouse?

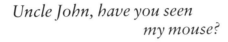

*Uncle John, have you seen
my mouse?*

Just a small sort of mouse, a dear little brown one,
He came from the country, he wasn't a town one,
So he'll feel all lonely in a London street;
Why, what could he possibly find to eat?

He must be somewhere. I'll ask Aunt Rose:
Have *you* seen a mouse with a woffelly nose?
Oh, somewhere about –
He's just got out …

Hasn't *anybody* seen my mouse?

Disobedience

James James
Morrison Morrison
Weatherby George Dupree
Took great
Care of his Mother,
Though he was only three.
James James
Said to his Mother,
"Mother," he said, said he;
"You must never go down to the end of the town, if you don't
  go down with me."

James James
Morrison's Mother
Put on a golden gown,
James James
Morrison's Mother
Drove to the end
          of the town.
James James
Morrison's Mother
Said to herself, said she:
"I can get right down to the end of the town
  and be back in time for tea."

King John
Put up a notice,
"LOST or STOLEN or STRAYED!
JAMES JAMES
MORRISON'S MOTHER
SEEMS TO HAVE BEEN MISLAID.
LAST SEEN
WANDERING VAGUELY:
QUITE OF HER OWN ACCORD,
SHE TRIED TO GET DOWN TO THE END OF
THE TOWN — FORTY SHILLINGS REWARD!

James James
Morrison Morrison
(Commonly known as Jim)
Told his
Other relations
Not to go blaming *him*.
James James
Said to his mother,
"Mother," he said, said he:
"You must *never* go down to the end of the town
without consulting me."

James James
Morrison's mother
Hasn't been heard of since.
King John
Said he was sorry,
So did the Queen and Prince.
King John
(Somebody told me)
Said to a man he knew:
"If people go down to the d of the town, well,
what can *anyone do*?"

(*Now then, very softly*)

J. J.
M. M.
W. G. Du P.
Took great
C/o his M★★★★
Though he was only 3.
J. J.
Said to his M★★★★★
"M★★★★★," he said, said he:
"You-must-never-go-down-to-the-end-of-the-town-if-
you-don't-go-down-with-ME!

The Three Foxes

Once upon a time there were three little foxes
Who didn't wear stockings, and they didn't wear sockses,
But they all had handkerchiefs to blow their noses,
And they kept their handkerchiefs in cardboard boxes.

They lived in the forest in three little houses,
And they didn't wear coats, and they didn't wear trousies.
They ran through the woods on their little bare tootsies,
And they played "Touch last" with a family of mouses.

They didn't go shopping in the
    High Street shopses,
But caught what they wanted
    in the woods and copses.
They all went fishing, and they caught
    three wormses,
They went out hunting, and they caught
    three wopses.

They went to a Fair, and they all won prizes –
Three plum-puddingses and three mince-pieses.
They rode on elephants and swang on swingses,
And hit three coco-nuts at coco-nut shieses.

That's all that I know of the three little foxes
Who kept their handkerchiefs in cardboard boxes.
They lived in the forest in three little houses,
But they didn't wear coats and they didn't wear trousies.
And they didn't wear stockings and they didn't wear sockses.

Market Square

I had a penny,
A bright new penny,
I took my penny
  To the market square.
I wanted a rabbit,
A little brown rabbit,
And I looked for a rabbit
  'Most everywhere.

For I went to the stall where they sold sweet lavender
(*"Only a penny for a bunch of lavender!"*).
"Have you got a rabbit, 'cos I don't want lavender?"
  But they hadn't got a rabbit, not anywhere there.

I had a penny,
And I had another penny,
I took my pennies
  To the market square.
I did want a rabbit,
A little baby rabbit,
And I looked for rabbits
  'Most everywhere.

And I went to the stall where
  they sold fresh mackerel
("*Now then! Tuppence for a
  fresh-caught mackerel!*").
"Have you got a rabbit, 'cos I
  don't like mackerel?"
But they hadn't got a rabbit,
  not anywhere there.

I found a sixpence,
A little white sixpence.
I took it in my hand
  To the market square.
I was buying my rabbit
(I do like rabbits),
And I looked for my rabbit
  'Most everywhere.

So I went to the stall where they sold fine saucepans
(*"Walk up, walk up, sixpence for a saucepan!"*).
"Could I have a rabbit, 'cos we've got two saucepans?"
  But they hadn't got a rabbit, not anywhere there.

I had nuffin',
No, I hadn't got nuffin',
So I didn't go down
  To the market square;
But I walked on the common
The old-gold common …
And I saw little rabbits
  'Most everywhere!

So I'm sorry for the people who sell fine saucepans,
I'm sorry for the people who sell fresh mackerel.
I'm sorry for the people who sell sweet lavender,
    'Cos they haven't got a rabbit, not anywhere there!

The Dormouse and the Doctor

There once was a Dormouse who lived in a bed
Of delphiniums (blue) and geraniums (red),
And all the day long he'd a wonderful view
Of geraniums (red) and delphiniums (blue).

A doctor came hurrying round, and he said:
"Tut-tut, I am sorry to find you in bed.
Just say 'Ninety-nine,' while I look at your chest ...
Don't you find that chrysanthemums answer the best?"

The Dormouse looked round at the view and replied
(When he'd said "Ninety-nine") that he'd tried and he'd tried,
And much the most answering things that he knew
Were geraniums (red) and delphiniums (blue).

The Doctor stood frowning and shaking his head,
And he took up his shiny silk hat as he said:
"What the patient requires is a change," and he went
To see some chrysanthemum people in Kent.

The Dormouse lay there, and he gazed at the view
Of geraniums (red) and delphiniums (blue),
And he knew there was nothing
       he wanted instead
Of delphiniums (blue) and geraniums (red).

The Doctor came back and, to show what he meant,
He had brought some chrysanthemum cuttings from Kent.
"Now *these*," he remarked, "give a *much* better view
Than geraniums (red) and delphiniums (blue)."

They took out their spades and they dug up the bed
Of delphiniums (blue) and geraniums (red),
And they planted chrysanthemums (yellow and white).
"And *now*," said the Doctor, "we'll *soon* have you right."

The Dormouse looked out, and he said with a sigh:
"I suppose all these people know better than I.
It was silly, perhaps, but I *did* like the view
Of geraniums (red) and delphiniums (blue)."

The Doctor came round and examined his chest,
And ordered him Nourishment, Tonics, and Rest.
"How very effective," he said, as he shook
The thermometer, "all these chrysanthemums look!"

  The Dormouse turned over to shut out
    the sight
  Of the endless chrysanthemums
    (yellow and white).
  "How lovely," he thought, "to be back in a bed
  Of delphiniums (blue) and geraniums (red)."

  The Doctor said, "Tut! It's another attack!"
  And ordered him Milk and Massage-of-the-back,
  And Freedom-from-worry and Drives-in-a-car,
  And murmured, "How sweet your
    chrysanthemums are!"

The Dormouse lay there with his paws
  to his eyes,
And imagined himself such a
  pleasant surprise:
"I'll *pretend* the chrysanthemums
  turn to a bed
Of delphiniums (blue) and
  geraniums (red)!"

The Doctor next morning was rubbing his hands,
And saying, "There's nobody quite understands
These cases as I do! The cure has begun!
How fresh the chrysanthemums look in the sun!"

The Dormouse lay happy, his eyes were so tight
He could see no chrysanthemums, yellow or white.
And all that he felt at the back of his head
Were delphiniums (blue) and geraniums (red).

And that is the reason (Aunt Emily said)
If a Dormouse gets in a chrysanthemum bed,
You will find (so Aunt Emily says) that he lies
Fast asleep on his front with his paws to his eyes.